★ ★ ALL ABOUT AMERICA ★ ★ ★

UNITED STATES STICKER BOOK

By Carol Benanti

Illustrated by Earl Dickens

Watermill Press

INTRODUCTION

How much do you know about the United States of America? You probably know there are 50 states in all. But did you know there are only three other countries larger in area than the United States? Those three nations are Russia, Canada, and the People's Republic of China.

Most people know that Washington, D.C. is the nation's capital. But did you know that the letters D.C. stand for "District of Columbia"? Washington, D.C. is only 69 square miles and is not part of any state. It is bordered on three sides by the state of Maryland, and on the fourth side by the state of Virginia.

Did you know only two countries share a border with the United States? To our south is Mexico, which borders California, Arizona, New Mexico, and Texas for approximately 1,950 miles. Canada shares a combined 5,525 mile-long border with the continental United States and the eastern border of Alaska.

Can you name the five Great Lakes? (Superior, Michigan, Huron, Erie, and Ontario.) These lakes form the greatest connected area of fresh water on Earth. And Lake Superior is the largest freshwater lake in the world!

The United States is sometimes called "Uncle Sam." Do you know why? During the War of 1812 against the British, a man named Samuel Wilson shipped supplies to the U.S. Army. Local workers called him "Uncle Sam," and stamped "U.S." on the barrels. Soldiers saw the stamp and used it as a nickname for the United States! In 1961, Congress passed a resolution recognizing Wilson as the namesake of our national nickname.

You'll learn much more about the United States in this exciting book. Each page is packed with fascinating information about each state. And don't forget to enjoy the stickers in the center of the book. Have fun exploring these great United States!

Alabama was once called the "Cotton State," and cotton was very important to its economy. But insects called *boll weevils* killed the cotton. These insects made the farmers realize they could raise other things, like livestock and peanuts. Now there is a monument to the boll weevil in the city of Enterprise!

Many young people visit Alabama to swim at the beach and to fish in the Gulf of Mexico. Ships from all over the world come to the port of Mobile. The U.S.S. Alabama is anchored in Mobile Bay.

The Alabama Space and Rocket Center in Huntsville holds the biggest collection of missiles and space equipment in the world. That's where they learned to build the rocket that put a man on the moon!

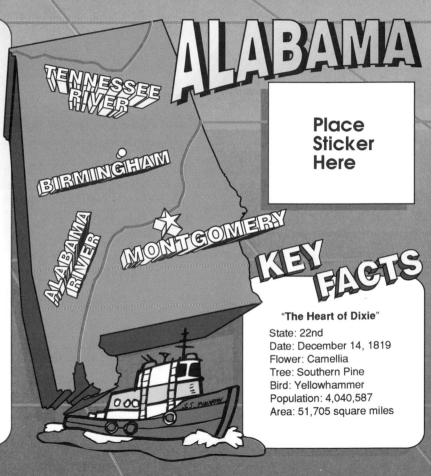

ALABAMA

Place Sticker Here

KEY FACTS

"The Heart of Dixie"

State: 22nd
Date: December 14, 1819
Flower: Camellia
Tree: Southern Pine
Bird: Yellowhammer
Population: 4,040,587
Area: 51,705 square miles

ALASKA

Place Sticker Here

YUKON RIVER

FAIRBANKS

JUNEAU

MT. McKINLEY

KEY FACTS

"The Last Frontier"

State: 49th
Date: January 3, 1959
Flower: Forget-Me-Not
Tree: Sitka Spruce
Bird: Willow Ptarmigan
Population: 550,043
Area: 591,004 square miles

Alaska is the largest state in the United States. The U.S. paid Russia about two cents an acre for it! However, Alaska has fewer people than any other state. Eskimos still hunt and fish the way they did many years ago.

Mount McKinley is the highest mountain in the U.S. It reaches 20,320 feet! Oil is Alaska's most important mineral product. The Alaskan Pipeline is 800 miles long and carries oil across the state.

In 1896, gold was discovered in the Yukon Territory. This started the famous Alaska Gold Rush. Many people moved to Alaska. Today people visit this beautiful state to see dog sled races, glaciers, and mountains. Others come to see the elk, caribou, moose, and bears.

One of the seven natural wonders of the world, the Grand Canyon is in the northwestern region of **Arizona**. It took millions of years for the canyon to form!

Arizona has many old western towns, ranches, and Native American reservations. It is the only place in the U.S. where you can stand in four states at once. "Four Corners" is where Arizona, Colorado, New Mexico, and Utah meet!

Arizona is dry and sunny during the day and cool at night. Since the end of World War II, the state's population has tripled. You can see logs turned to stone in the Petrified Forest National Park.

Arizona has 15 national monuments, more than any other state!

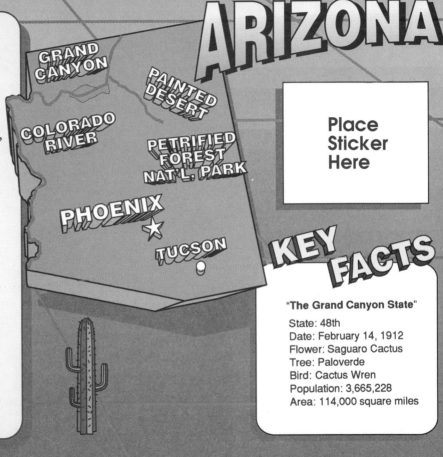

ARIZONA

GRAND CANYON

PAINTED DESERT

COLORADO RIVER

PETRIFIED FOREST NAT'L. PARK

PHOENIX ★

TUCSON

Place Sticker Here

KEY FACTS

"The Grand Canyon State"

State: 48th
Date: February 14, 1912
Flower: Saguaro Cactus
Tree: Paloverde
Bird: Cactus Wren
Population: 3,665,228
Area: 114,000 square miles

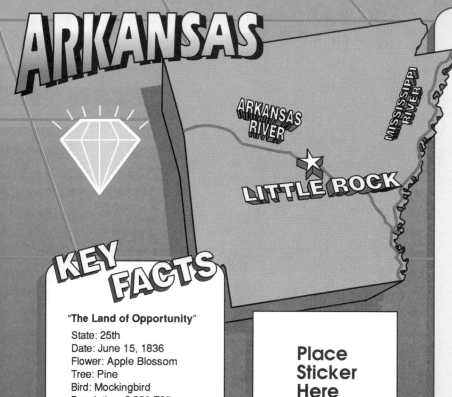

ARKANSAS

ARKANSAS RIVER

MISSISSIPPI RIVER

★ LITTLE ROCK

Place Sticker Here

America's only diamond mine is in **Arkansas**. The mine is in the remains of an ancient volcano near the city of Murfreesboro. You can hunt for diamonds there in Crater of Diamonds State Park!

Many people come to Arkansas every year to visit Hot Springs National Park. Some people think the springs have healing powers!

You can see people work at crafts and hear them play mountain music at the Ozark Folk Center near Mountain View.

Agriculture is an important part of the economy. The state is a leader in the production of rice, cotton, soybeans, and chickens!

Gold was found in **California** in 1848. People came from all over the world to dig for gold, and today more people live in California than in any other state. Only Alaska and Texas have more square miles than California.

Over 200 different fruit and vegetable crops are grown in California. Almost all the commercial almonds, dates, kiwi fruit, olives, and walnuts are grown there.

Los Angeles is famous for its movie industry. Many people visit Hollywood and Disneyland every year. The famous San Diego Zoo has one of the largest collections of animals and birds in the world.

The world's tallest trees – and largest living things – are California's giant redwoods.

Place Sticker Here

"The Golden State"
State: 31st
Date: September 9, 1850
Flower: Golden Poppy
Tree: California Redwood
Bird: California Valley Quail
Population: 29,760,021
Area: 158,706 square miles

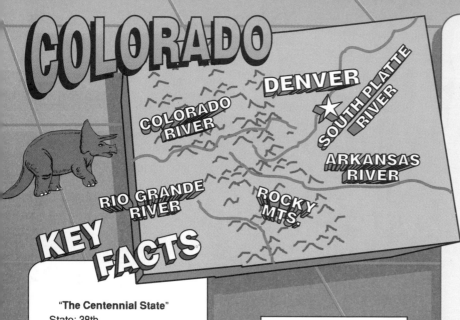

COLORADO

KEY FACTS

"The Centennial State"
State: 38th
Date: August 1, 1876
Flower: Rocky Mountain
　　　　Columbine
Tree: Blue Spruce
Bird: Lark Bunting
Population: 3,294,394
Area: 104,091 square miles

Place Sticker Here

Colorado, the highest state, is world famous for its ski resorts. Hundreds of mountains in Colorado are over 10,000 feet high! Pikes Peak is probably the most famous mountain in Colorado. Katherine Lee Bates wrote "America the Beautiful" after seeing the view from the top of Pikes Peak!

Colorado is known for its mountain scenery. Many mountain climbers and campers visit Colorado every summer. Mesa Verde National Park contains Native American cliff dwellings. These dwellings were mysteriously abandoned 700 years ago, and the park shows four different ways people lived from 1 A.D. to 1300 A.D.!

Every year many people go to the resorts at Aspen and Vail to enjoy snow skiing.

Connecticut is one of the smallest states. It had the first formal rules for government in the United States. These rules helped delegates at the Continental Congress create the Constitution.

Many people travel to Connecticut to visit Mystic Seaport and its 100-year-old ships. A nuclear-powered submarine can be seen in the city of Groton. The Whitfield House, a stone house built in 1639, is in Guilford.

Delaware was the first state in the United States, because it was the first to accept and sign the Constitution!

Delaware's laws are good for businesses, so the headquarters of many large companies are here. Teflon is made here.

Many colonial homes in Delaware are still lived in. The Winterthur Museum has more than 100 rooms of early furniture, china, and silver from 1640-1840!

CONNECTICUT RIVER

HARTFORD

CONNECTICUT

Place Sticker Here

KEY FACTS

"The Constitution State"

State: 5th
Date: January 9, 1788
Flower: Mountain Laurel
Tree: White Oak
Bird: Robin
Population: 3,287,116
Area: 5,018 square miles

DELAWARE RIVER

DOVER

DELAWARE

Place Sticker Here

KEY FACTS

"The First State"

State: 1st
Date: December 7, 1787
Flower: Peach Blossom
Tree: American Holly
Bird: Blue Hen Chicken
Population: 666,168
Area: 2,044 square miles

FLORIDA

TALLAHASSEE

ORLANDO

CAPE CANAVERAL

MIAMI

KEY WEST

Place Sticker Here

KEY FACTS

"The Sunshine State"

State: 27th
Date: March 3, 1845
Flower: Orange Blossom
Tree: Sabal Palm
Bird: Mockingbird
Population: 11,366,000
Area: 58,664 square miles

Because **Florida** has beautiful beaches and year-round sunny weather, tourism is its major industry. Many special attractions, like Walt Disney World and Universal Studios, bring millions of people to Florida every year!

The Kennedy Space Center, located at Cape Canaveral, is the United States center for space research. The space shuttles are launched here!

Hot summers and mild winters, combined with flat land, make Florida perfect for growing citrus. Two thirds of the world's oranges and grapefruits are grown in Florida.

The Everglades are one of the larges swamps in the world, and are filled with unusual tropical plants and wildlife. You can see alligators, manatees, herons, and bald eagles here.

Georgia is the largest state east of the Mississippi River. Its capital, Atlanta, is an important center for business. The first *Coca-Cola* was served in an Atlanta drugstore in 1887!

The Confederate Memorial of the Civil War, one of the world's largest sculptures, is just outside Atlanta. It is carved into the side of Stone Mountain, and shows Robert E. Lee, Stonewall Jackson, and Jefferson Davis on horseback.

More peanuts are grown in Georgia than in any other state. Farmers also grow tobacco, pecans, peaches, and corn. The Okefenokee Swamp, in southern Georgia, is the largest preserved freshwater swamp in the United States. It is a sanctuary for endangered wildlife!

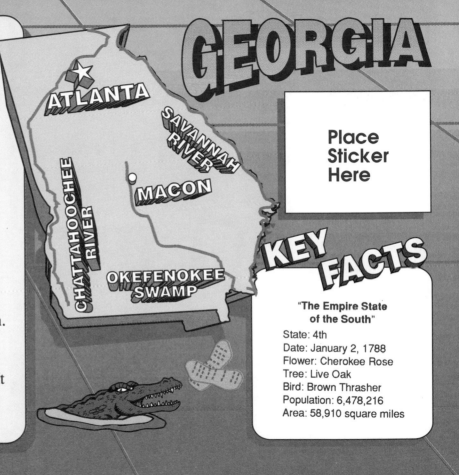

GEORGIA

Place Sticker Here

KEY FACTS

"The Empire State of the South"

State: 4th
Date: January 2, 1788
Flower: Cherokee Rose
Tree: Live Oak
Bird: Brown Thrasher
Population: 6,478,216
Area: 58,910 square miles

HAWAII

MAUI

OAHU

HONOLULU

HAWAII

KEY FACTS

"The Aloha State"
State: 50th
Date: August 21, 1959
Flower: Hibiscus
Tree: Kukui
Bird: Nene
    (Hawaiian Goose)
Population: 1,108,229
Area: 6,471 square miles

Place Sticker Here

Hawaii is the only state in the United States completely surrounded by water. It is made up of 132 islands, stretching over 1,500 miles in the Pacific Ocean. The islands were formed by volcanoes long ago. There are eight main islands.

The scenic waterfalls, palm trees, flowers, and the weather in Hawaii are world-famous. The beaches are noted for surfing. Most of the people in Hawaii live on the island of Oahu.

IDAHO

POTATOES

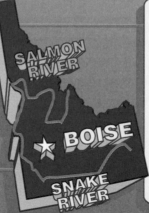

SALMON RIVER

BOISE

SNAKE RIVER

KEY FACTS

"The Gem State"
State: 43rd
Date: July 3, 1890
Flower: Syringa
Tree: Western White Pine
Bird: Mountain Bluebird
Population: 1,006,749
Area: 83,564 square miles

Place Sticker Here

Idaho is full of beautiful mountains, lakes, and rivers. People go there to hunt deer and elk, and to catch enormous trout and salmon. This Rocky Mountain state grows more potatoes than any other! Idaho is also the country's leading producer of silver.

Most of Idaho's electricity comes from *water*! The many dams on its rivers generate electric power for homes and businesses.

The world's tallest building is the Sears Tower in Chicago, **Illinois**. It is 110 stories high! Chicago is the third largest city in the United States, and O'Hare International Airport in Chicago is one of the busiest in the world.

Illinois has many museums and historical sites to visit. Abraham Lincoln's home is in Springfield. Illinois farms raise corn, hogs, and cattle.

People from **Indiana** are called "Hoosiers," supposedly because early settlers there asked, "Who's here?"

The *Indianapolis 500* is a famous car race held every year. More people attend this race than any other sports event in the country!

Wyandotte Cave is one of the largest in the country, with 35 miles of underground rooms and passageways!

ILLINOIS
KEY FACTS

Place Sticker Here

"The Land of Lincoln"
State: 21st
Date: December 3, 1818
Flower: Violet
Tree: White Oak
Bird: Cardinal
Population: 11,430,602
Area: 56,345 square miles

INDIANA
KEY FACTS

Place Sticker Here

"The Hoosier State"
State: 19th
Date: December 11, 1816
Flower: Peony
Tree: Tulip Tree
Bird: Cardinal
Population: 5,544,159
Area: 36,185 square miles

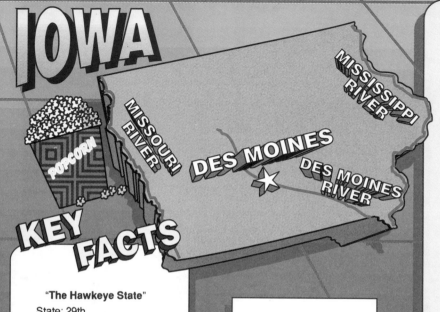

IOWA

MISSOURI RIVER

MISSISSIPPI RIVER

DES MOINES

DES MOINES RIVER

POPCORN

KEY FACTS

"The Hawkeye State"

State: 29th
Date: December 28, 1846
Flower: Wild Rose
Tree: Oak
Bird: Eastern Goldfinch
Population: 2,776,755
Area: 56,275 square miles

Place
Sticker
Here

Iowa is the only state bounded by two rivers that ships can travel on! The Mississippi River is on the east side of the state, and the Missouri River is on the west. All of the rivers in Iowa flow into the Mississippi-Missouri river system.

Iowa has some of the best farmland in the United States. People come from many different countries to farm in Iowa. It is the leading state in the production of hogs and corn, and is the second largest producer of soybeans. The biggest popcorn-processing plant in the nation is in Sioux City!

The Iowa State Fair is one of the largest in the United States, and takes place every August. The plains of the Midwest form one of the world's most productive agricultural regions!

Great herds of buffalo once roamed the **Kansas** plains. "Buffalo Bill" Cody got his nickname in Kansas when he shot over 4,000 buffalo to feed railroad workers! Now Kansas grows more wheat than any other state. It grows so much wheat that it is called the "Breadbasket of America."

Dodge City, Wichita, and Abilene, where President Eisenhower spent his childhood, are old western frontier towns. Front Street in Dodge City looks just as it did when cowboys rode their horses into town. Today in Dodge City you can see cowboys herd cattle on motorcycles!

Kansas is midway between the Atlantic Ocean and the Pacific Ocean. For this reason, another nickname for Kansas is "Midway, U.S.A."

KANSAS

KANSAS CITY

★ TOPEKA

DODGE CITY

SANTA FE TRAIL

ARKANSAS RIVER

KEY FACTS

Place Sticker Here

"The Sunflower State"
State: 34th
Date: January 29, 1861
Flower: Sunflower
Tree: Cottonwood
Bird: Western Meadowlark
Population: 2,477,574
Area: 82,277 square miles

KENTUCKY

★ FRANKFORT
• LEXINGTON

OHIO RIVER

KENTUCKY RIVER

TENNESSEE RIVER

CUMBERLAND GAP →

KEY FACTS

"The Bluegrass State"
State: 15th
Date: June 1, 1792
Flower: Goldenrod
Tree: Kentucky Coffeetree
Bird: Kentucky Cardinal
Population: 3,685,296
Area: 40,409 square miles

Place Sticker Here

Kentucky is famous for raising race horses at over 350 thoroughbred horse farms. The Kentucky Derby is the oldest and most exciting horse race in the United States. People come from all over the world to see the "Derby" every May at Churchill Downs in Louisville.

Kentucky has many famous old homes. You can see where our 16th President was born at the Abraham Lincoln Birthplace National Historic Site. You can visit Civil War battlefields, a reconstructed fort at Boonesborough State Park, and many other historic attractions.

Visit Mammoth Cave National Park, with its 300 miles of passages, waterfalls, underground rivers, and lakes. You can also visit Fort Knox, where the United States stores most of its gold!

Baton Rouge, **Louisiana's** capital, means "red stick" in French. Native Americans first marked this city by painting a tree trunk red!

New Orleans, which is on the Mississippi River, is Louisiana's largest city. You can take a steamboat ride on the Mississippi River. Jazz got its start in New Orleans' French Quarter in the early 1900's. The French and Spanish buildings there look like they did 200 years ago! A statue of Andrew Jackson on horseback is in Jackson Square. The French Quarter is famous for its annual *Mardi Gras* celebration.

Louisiana is shaped like a boot. The many rivers, lakes, and bayous (slow-moving river inlets or outlets) make fishing very popular. The Mississippi Delta has the richest farmland in the state.

RED RIVER

SABINE RIVER

CALCASIEU RIVER

MISSISSIPPI RIVER

PEARL RIVER

LOUISIANA

BATON ROUGE

NEW ORLEANS

KEY FACTS

Place Sticker Here

"The Pelican State"

State: 18th
Date: April 30, 1812
Flower: Magnolia
Tree: Bald Cypress
Bird: Brown Pelican
Population: 4,219,973
Area: 47,752 square miles

MAINE

ST. CROIX RIVER

PENOBSCOT RIVER

KENNEBEC RIVER

★ AUGUSTA

PORTLAND

Place Sticker Here

KEY FACTS

"The Pine Tree State"
State: 23rd
Date: March 15, 1820
Flower: White Pine Cone
and Tassel
Tree: White Pine
Bird: Chickadee
Population: 1,227,928
Area: 33,265 square miles

Maine is farther east than any other state, so people here see the sun rise before anyone else in the country! Maine's beautiful shoreline supplies the country with more than 80 percent of all its lobster!

Known for its rocky beaches, Maine is also famous for its many lighthouses. You can visit Portland Head Light, one of the oldest and most famous lighthouses in the United States. President George Washington had it buil in 1790 to guide boats at sea!

People come to Maine to climb and ski its mountains, hunt in the beautiful forests, and fish in the lakes. Acadia National Park is the only national park where the mountains meet the sea!

Many rivers run into Chesapeake Bay, which almost cuts **Maryland** in half. Millions of pounds of seafood are caught in the Bay every year!

During the Civil War, Maryland was divided between the North, or the Union states, and the South, which was made up of the Confederate states. However, President Abraham Lincoln forced Maryland to stay in the Union because Washington D.C., the Union's capital, was in Maryland.

Maryland is the home of the United States Naval Academy at Annapolis. The Fort McHenry National Monument is a historic landmark. Francis Scott Key wrote "The Star Spangled Banner" about the battle for this fort in 1814!

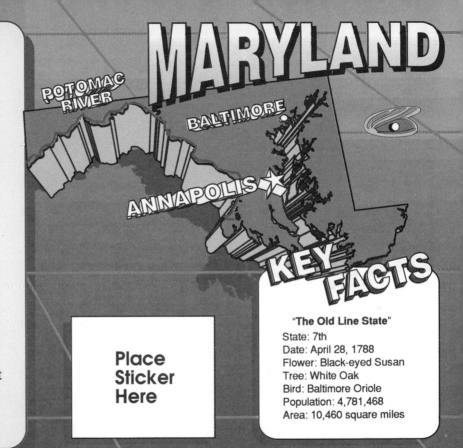

MARYLAND

POTOMAC RIVER

BALTIMORE

ANNAPOLIS ★

KEY FACTS

Place Sticker Here

"The Old Line State"
State: 7th
Date: April 28, 1788
Flower: Black-eyed Susan
Tree: White Oak
Bird: Baltimore Oriole
Population: 4,781,468
Area: 10,460 square miles

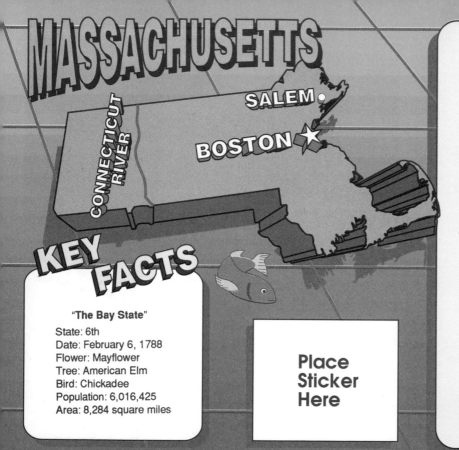

MASSACHUSETTS

SALEM •

BOSTON ☆

CONNECTICUT RIVER

KEY FACTS

"The Bay State"

State: 6th
Date: February 6, 1788
Flower: Mayflower
Tree: American Elm
Bird: Chickadee
Population: 6,016,425
Area: 8,284 square miles

Place Sticker Here

American history books are filled with facts about **Massachusetts**. Visit Plymouth, where the Pilgrims landed in 1620. Visit Boston to see Paul Revere's house, and go to Boston Harbor, the site of the Boston Tea Party in 1773.

During the Industrial Revolution in the United States, Massachusetts became a leading manufacturer. It still is today, producing electrical equipment and other kinds of machinery. Fishing is also very important to the economy, and the waters around Massachusetts yield large amounts of sea scallops.

You can see Harvard University, the first college in the colonies. It was founded in 1636 in Cambridge.

The "hook" of Massachusetts is called Cape Cod, where there are quaint historic towns like Provincetown.

Michigan is the only state divided into two parts. It is also the only state that touches four of the five Great Lakes! People come from all over the country to camp, hunt, fish, ski, swim, and boat on Michigan's 11,000 natural lakes.

More cars and trucks are built in Detroit, Michigan, than anywhere else in the country. Detroit, Michigan's largest city, is known as "Motor City."

Snowmobiling, tobogganing, and ice fishing are popular in the the upper portion of Michigan during winter. There are about 150 waterfalls and many forests. This is where the Porcupine Mountains and iron and copper mines are found.

Battle Creek produces more breakfast cereal than any other U.S. city!

MICHIGAN

PORCUPINE MTS.

GRAND RAPIDS · LANSING · DETROIT

Place Sticker Here

KEY FACTS

"The Wolverine State"
State: 26th
Date: January 26, 1837
Flower: Apple Blossom
Tree: White Pine
Bird: Robin
Population: 9,295,297
Area: 58,527 square miles

MINNESOTA

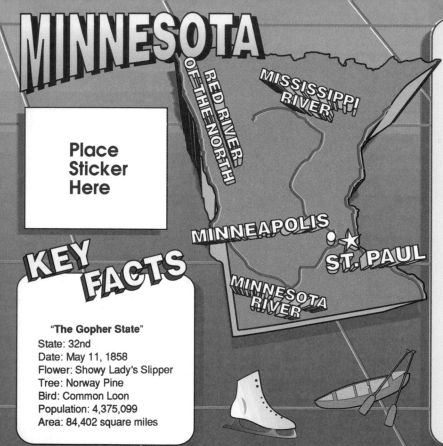

Place Sticker Here

KEY FACTS

"The Gopher State"
State: 32nd
Date: May 11, 1858
Flower: Showy Lady's Slipper
Tree: Norway Pine
Bird: Common Loon
Population: 4,375,099
Area: 84,402 square miles

RED RIVER OF THE NORTH

MISSISSIPPI RIVER

MINNEAPOLIS

ST. PAUL

MINNESOTA RIVER

Millions of people come to **Minnesota**, "The Land of 10,000 Lakes," to vacation every year. Minnesota's forests are great for camping and hunting, and there are more than 15,000 lakes for boating.

Minnesota mines produce more than two thirds of the iron ore in the United States. Huge cargo ships sail from Duluth and across Lake Superior to carry the ore to steel mills all over the world.

Visit Fort Snelling near St. Paul. This old military post was built in the 1820's, and you can see what military life was like back then.

Near Brainerd is a pioneer lumbering village called Lumbertown, U.S.A.

Mississippi's west boundary is the Mississippi River. This land was once very swampy, but artificial riverbanks called "levees" were built to keep the rising waters from washing away farms.

There are many beautiful pre-Civil War mansions and plantations to see in Mississippi. You can visit Florewood River Plantation and see how people lived on a cotton plantation before the Civil War! There is also a museum and state park there.

You can see many old forts in Mississippi, like the Old Spanish Fort and Singing River at Pascagoula. You can also take a riverboat ride down the river!

This state is a major cotton producer.

MISSISSIPPI

Place Sticker Here

KEY FACTS

"The Magnolia State"

State: 20th
Date: December 10, 1817
Flower: Magnolia
Tree: Magnolia
Bird: Mockingbird
Population: 2,573,216
Area: 47,689 square miles

MISSOURI

KEY FACTS

"The Show Me State"

State: 24th
Date: August 10, 1821
Flower: Hawthorn
Tree: Flowering Dogwood
Bird: Bluebird
Population: 5,117,073
Area: 69,697 square miles

KANSAS CITY

MISSOURI RIVER

ST. LOUIS

JEFFERSON CITY

MISSISSIPPI RIVER

OZARK MTS.

Place Sticker Here

Missouri is a center for travel because the Mississippi and Missouri rivers, the two longest rivers in the country, meet there. The Santa Fe Trail and the Oregon Trail both start in Independence.

The tallest monument in the world is the Gateway to the West arch, in St. Louis. The arch is 630 feet high, and symbolizes the role St. Louis played in settling the old West.

You can visit the Pony Express Stables and Museum at St. Joseph. Go to Hannibal to see Mark Twain's Boyhood Home and Museum!

A popular vacation spot is the Ozark Mountains, with their many deep caves. The Ozarks are also known for their rapid streams and large springs.

State Flag Stickers

WISCONSIN

VERMONT

SOUTH DAKOTA

OREGON

NORTH CAROLINA

NEW HAMPSHIRE

WYOMING

VIRGINIA

TENNESSEE

PENNSYLVANIA

NORTH DAKOTA

NEW JERSEY

WASHINGTON

TEXAS

RHODE ISLAND

OHIO

NEW MEXICO

WEST VIRGINIA

UTAH

SOUTH CAROLINA

OKLAHOMA

NEW YORK

MISSOURI

MINNESOTA

KENTUCKY

ILLINOIS

FLORIDA

CALIFORNIA

ALABAMA

MONTANA

MISSISSIPPI

LOUISIANA

INDIANA

GEORGIA

COLORADO

ALASKA

NEBRASKA

MARYLAND

MICHIGAN

IOWA

HAWAII

CONNECTICUT

ARIZONA

NEVADA

MASSACHUSETTS

MAINE

KANSAS

IDAHO

DELAWARE

ARKANSAS

MONTANA

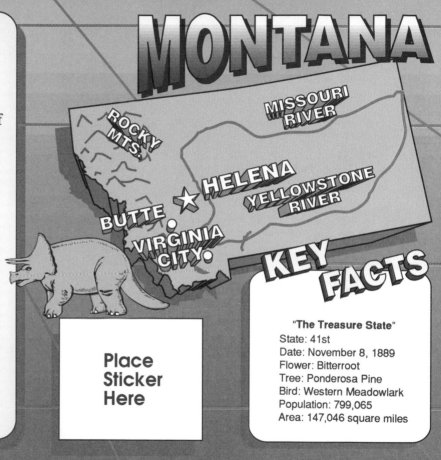

Montana has beautiful mountains and parks. Glacier National Park has more than 50 glaciers on its mountains. If you visit the park you may see grizzly bears, cougars, mountain goats, or bighorn sheep.

You can also visit Little Big Horn River. This is the site of "Custer's Last Stand," where General Custer and his men were defeated by Chief Sitting Bull and the Sioux and Cheyenne Indians.

There are several Native American reservations, where you can see traditional crafts and ceremonies. Montana is also known for its dude ranches, ghosts towns, and rodeos, where famous riders compete for prizes.

Place Sticker Here

KEY FACTS

"The Treasure State"
State: 41st
Date: November 8, 1889
Flower: Bitterroot
Tree: Ponderosa Pine
Bird: Western Meadowlark
Population: 799,065
Area: 147,046 square miles

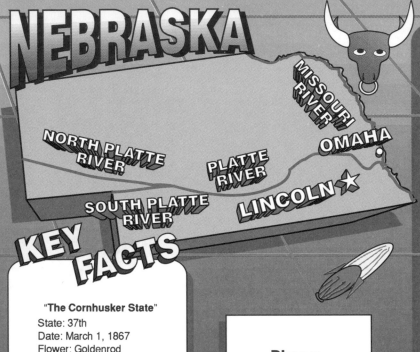

NEBRASKA

Place Sticker Here

Nebraska, also known as "The Tree Planter's State," is where the first Arbor Day was celebrated in 1872. Once called the "Great American Desert," Nebraska didn't have enough trees for early settlers to build homes. They had to use sod to build their houses. They planted trees for lumber, fruit, and shade. Now people plant trees all over the United States on Arbor Day!

Nebraska's farms are leaders in wheat, hay, and corn production, and Omaha is the leading meat-packing city in the United States. Did you know that the only two national forests completely planted by people are in Nebraska?

You can visit Fort Niobrara National Wildlife Refuge to see buffalo and many other wild animals.

Nevada is the driest state in the United States, usually getting less than ten inches of rain per year! It is mostly mountains and deserts.

You can visit many old mining towns and see how they looked in the 1800's. Millions of dollars of gold and silver came out of the Comstock Lode between 1859 and 1880!

Today, millions of people still go to Nevada to strike it rich in the casinos of Las Vegas. Called the "Entertainment and Gambling Capital of the World," Nevada is the only western state where gambling is legal! People come from all over to see spectacular shows in "Vegas."

The Hoover Dam, near Las Vegas, is the world's largest dam, providing electric power to three states!

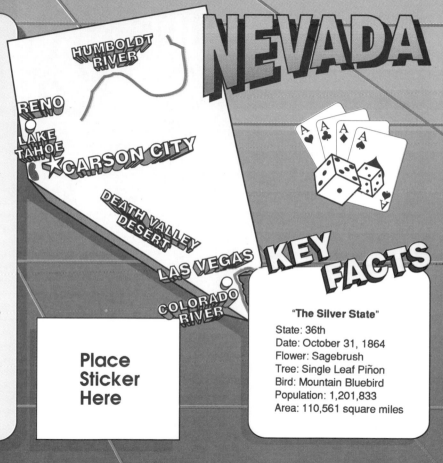

NEVADA

HUMBOLDT RIVER

RENO

LAKE TAHOE

★ CARSON CITY

DEATH VALLEY DESERT

LAS VEGAS

COLORADO RIVER

KEY FACTS

"The Silver State"

State: 36th
Date: October 31, 1864
Flower: Sagebrush
Tree: Single Leaf Piñon
Bird: Mountain Bluebird
Population: 1,201,833
Area: 110,561 square miles

Place Sticker Here

NEW HAMPSHIRE

Place Sticker Here

KEY FACTS

"The Granite State"
State: 9th
Date: June 21, 1788
Flower: Purple Lilac
Tree: White Birch
Bird: Purple Finch
Population: 1,109,252
Area: 9,297 square miles

WHITE MTS.

CONNECTICUT RIVER

CONCORD
★
MANCHESTER

New Hampshire was the first colony to set up its own government. Six months before the Declaration of Independence was signed, New Hampshire adopted a constitution! After the Revolutionary War, the new U.S. Constitution needed 9 of the 13 states to agree to it. New Hampshire was the ninth state, and the United States became a reality!

In 1719, New Hampshire farmers planted the first potatoes in the country. In 1830, Sarah Josepha Hale wrote "Mary Had a Little Lamb" in a little red schoolhouse in Newport!

One of the most important industries in New Hampshire is tourism. People visit every year to ski and hike in the mountains. Some people come to New Hampshire in autumn to see the leaves turn bright orange, red, and yellow.

NEW JERSEY

Although **New Jersey** is the fifth smallest state, it has the most people per square mile! New Jersey shares the Hudson River with New York, and the Delaware River with Philadelphia. Many of its products are shipped all over the world from these ports.

New Jersey's Atlantic shore is known for its great beaches. Famous Atlantic City is known for its long boardwalk and gambling casinos. Did you know that the property names in the game *Monopoly* are named after streets in Atlantic City?

In 1879, Thomas Edison invented the electric light bulb at his laboratory in Menlo Park.

Place Sticker Here

KEY FACTS

"The Garden State"
State: 3rd
Date: December 18, 1787
Flower: Purple Violet
Tree: Red Oak
Bird: Eastern Goldfinch
Population: 7,730,188
Area: 7,787 square miles

NEW MEXICO

ROCKY MTS.

★ SANTA FE

• ALBUQUERQUE

RIO GRANDE RIVER

PECOS RIVER

WHITE SANDS DESERT

CARLSBAD CAVERNS

KEY FACTS

"The Land of Enchantment"

State: 47th
Date: January 6, 1912
Flower: Yucca
Tree: Piñon
Bird: Roadrunner
Population: 1,515,069
Area: 121,593 square miles

Place Sticker Here

Dry and sunny **New Mexico** has been a center for space and nuclear research for many years. The first atom bomb was set off in New Mexico in 1945! Robert H. Goddard, the "father of the modern rocket," experimented with rockets in the New Mexico desert.

New Mexico is a very exciting place to visit. There are many *pueblos*, which are Native American homes built into cliffs. Many people come to New Mexico to see Native American ceremonies. Many towns have annual rodeos!

You can visit Spanish missions and go to Spanish festivals, called *fiestas*. You can explore huge caves at Carlsbad Caverns National Park. Thousands of bats fly in these caves!

Mining is an important industry to New Mexico.

New York City was the first capital of the United States, and is now the most populated city in the country. **New York** is the country's center for the arts and business.

You can see the Statue of Liberty in New York Harbor, the Empire State Building, Radio City Music Hall, and legendary Broadway! Visit the American Museum of Natural History, the United Nations, the Hayden Planetarium, the Metropolitan Museum of Art, the Bronx Zoo, and Central Park!

Niagara Falls, which borders Canada and the U.S., is the most famous waterfall in the world! New York state also has many scenic mountains, lakes, and rivers.

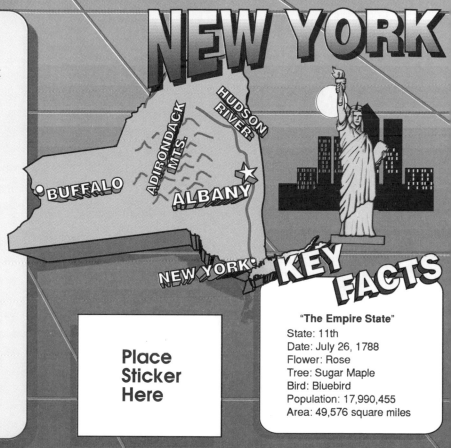

NEW YORK

BUFFALO

ADIRONDACK MTS.

HUDSON RIVER

ALBANY

NEW YORK

KEY FACTS

"The Empire State"
State: 11th
Date: July 26, 1788
Flower: Rose
Tree: Sugar Maple
Bird: Bluebird
Population: 17,990,455
Area: 49,576 square miles

Place Sticker Here

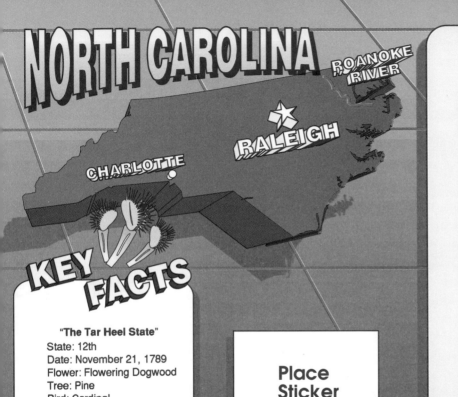

NORTH CAROLINA

ROANOKE RIVER

RALEIGH

CHARLOTTE

KEY FACTS

"The Tar Heel State"
State: 12th
Date: November 21, 1789
Flower: Flowering Dogwood
Tree: Pine
Bird: Cardinal
Population: 6,628,637
Area: 52,669 square miles

Place Sticker Here

Great Smoky Mountains National Park is on the border of Tennessee and **North Carolina**. Part of the Appalachian Mountains, the "Smoky's" were named because they are covered with a blue haze. The haze comes from the conifer trees, which release hydrocarbons!

North Carolina is the nation's leading producer of wooden furniture. Many famous battlefields from the Revolutionary War and Civil War are in North Carolina.

The tallest lighthouse in the country is the Cape Hatteras Lighthouse. Kitty Hawk, also on North Carolina's seashore, is where the Wright Brothers flew the first powered airplane! A national monument honoring the Wright Brothers now stands here.

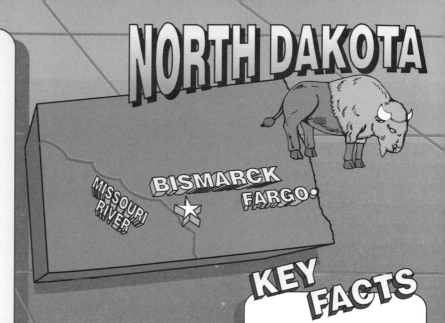

NORTH DAKOTA

Huge cattle ranches, sheep ranches, and farms are all over **North Dakota**. The economy depends on agriculture more than any other state except South Dakota. Despite the dry climate and short growing season, North Dakota produces more wheat than any other state except Kansas.

North Dakota has many Native American reservations. People visit the famous Badlands, which are strange shapes of clay, shale, and sandstone formed thousands of years ago by wind and water! The Badlands were given their name by early travelers who found this region difficult to cross.

MISSOURI RIVER
BISMARCK
FARGO

Place Sticker Here

KEY FACTS

"The Flickertail State"
State: 39th
Date: November 2, 1889
Flower: Wild Prairie Rose
Tree: American Elm
Bird: Western Meadowlark
Population: 638,800
Area: 70,702 square miles

OHIO

TOLEDO • CLEVELAND

★ COLUMBUS

CINCINNATI • OHIO RIVER

KEY FACTS

"The Buckeye State"

State: 17th
Date: March 1, 1803
Flower: Scarlet Carnation
Tree: Buckeye
Bird: Cardinal
Population: 10,847,115
Area: 41,330 square miles

Place Sticker Here

Ohio is a leader in manufacturing iron, steel, rubber goods, machinery, and auto parts. Baseballs, footballs, and metal toys are also made in Ohio! The National Professional Football Hall of Fame is in Canton, and the Cincinnati Red Stockings became the country's first professional baseball team in 1869.

There are thousands of lakes to fish and swim in, and there are many historical sites. Seven United States Presidents were born in Ohio! Thomas Edison, John Glenn, and Neil Armstrong were also born here.

Ohio lies between the Ohio River and Lake Erie, and many roads, railways, and canals cross these major water routes. This has made Ohio a leader in industrial manufacturing.

Oklahoma was hit by a drought in the1930's, and much dry land was blown away by the wind. This caused huge "dirt" storms, and Oklahoma was nicknamed the "Dust Bowl." The summers here are usually long and hot.

More than 60 Native American tribes live in Oklahoma. The state's name comes from the Choctaw Indian words "okla," meaning *people*, and "humma," meaning *red*. Oklahoma is a major center of Native American culture.

You can see many exciting rodeos in Oklahoma, including the National Finals Rodeo in Tulsa. The National Cowboy Hall of Fame and Western Heritage Center exhibit western paintings and sculptures. The Rodeo Hall of Fame is at the center.

OKLAHOMA

TULSA

ARKANSAS RIVER

OKLAHOMA CITY

RED RIVER

KEY FACTS

"The Sooner State"

State: 46th
Date: November 16, 1907
Flower: Mistletoe
Tree: Redbud
Bird: Scissor-tailed Flycatcher
Population: 3,145,585
Area: 69,956 square miles

Place Sticker Here

OREGON

PORTLAND

★ SALEM

CASCADE MOUNTAINS

KEY FACTS

"The Beaver State"
State: 33rd
Date: February 14, 1859
Flower: Oregon Grape
Tree: Douglas Fir
Bird: Western Meadowlark
Population: 2,842,321
Area: 97,073 square miles

Place Sticker Here

Millions of people visit **Oregon** every year to see the beautiful mountains, valleys, and forests. Oregon leads the country in lumber production. Nearly half the state is covered with dense forests, and you can see lumberjacks cutting down tall trees! Hunting, skiing, and fishing are also popular.

You can see hundreds of sea lions in their natural setting at the Sea Lion Caves, near Florence. Crater Lake, in the Cascade Mountains, is the deepest lake in the country. It is at the top of a dead volcano, and it is 1,932 feet deep!

Many laws have been passed in Oregon to keep its land, water, and air clean. Visitors can drive along the Columbia River Gorge, the Bonneville Dam, and Multnomah Falls.

Many tourists visit **Pennsylvania** every year to see its historic sites. Independence National Historic Park, in Philadelphia, includes Independence Hall and the Liberty Bell.

Gettysburg National Military Park is where the famous Battle of Gettysburg was fought. It is also where Abraham Lincoln delivered his famous Gettysburg Address. You can visit the home of Betsy Ross, who, according to legend, made the first United States flag.

Hershey, Pennsylvania, is the home of the world's largest chocolate factory. The city's main streets are Cocoa Avenue and Chocolate Avenue!

In the Pennsylvania Dutch part of the state, you can see people riding in horse-drawn buggies!

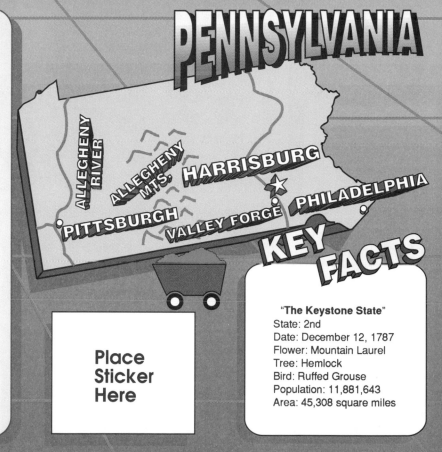

PENNSYLVANIA

ALLEGHENY RIVER

ALLEGHENY MTS.

HARRISBURG

PITTSBURGH

VALLEY FORGE

PHILADELPHIA

KEY FACTS

Place Sticker Here

"The Keystone State"
State: 2nd
Date: December 12, 1787
Flower: Mountain Laurel
Tree: Hemlock
Bird: Ruffed Grouse
Population: 11,881,643
Area: 45,308 square miles

RHODE ISLAND

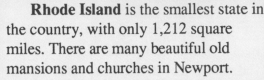

BLACKSTONE RIVER

PROVIDENCE

KEY FACTS

"Ocean State"
State: 13th
Date: May 29, 1790
Flower: Violet
Tree: Red Maple
Bird: Rhode Island Red
Population: 1,003,464
Area: 1,212 square miles

Place Sticker Here

Rhode Island is the smallest state in the country, with only 1,212 square miles. There are many beautiful old mansions and churches in Newport.

In 1854 a new breed of chicken was developed in Rhode Island and named the Rhode Island Red!

You can visit the Slater Mill Historic Site, which is a 1793 yarn mill with early textile machines in Pawtucket.

SOUTH CAROLINA

COLUMBIA

KEY FACTS

"The Palmetto State"
State: 8th
Date: May 23, 1788
Flower: Carolina Jessamine
Tree: Palmetto
Bird: Carolina Wren
Population: 3,486,703
Area: 31,113 square miles

Place Sticker Here

South Carolina is known for its beautiful plantations and pre-Civil War mansions. The Civil War began on April 12, 1861 in Charleston, at Fort Sumter.

Charleston has always been a big port. The first museum and musical society in the United States were founded in Charleston.

South Carolina is a leading producer of tobacco, peaches, and textiles.

South Dakota is the home of the largest gold mine in the United States. Its economy depends on agriculture more than any other state. There are rodeos, fairs, ghost towns, and all the excitment of frontier life in South Dakota.

The Black Hills are in the southwest corner of the state. From a distance the hills look black, but they are actually covered with thick pine forests. Beautiful Mount Rushmore National Memorial is in the Black Hills. Carved into the mountain are the faces of George Washington, Thomas Jefferson, Theodore Roosevelt, and Abraham Lincoln.

You can also visit Dinosaur Park in Rapid City, where you can see life-sized cement dinosaurs!

SOUTH DAKOTA

PIERRE

MISSOURI RIVER

SIOUX FALLS

KEY FACTS

Place Sticker Here

"The Sunshine State"
State: 40th
Date: November 2, 1889
Flower: American Pasqueflower
Tree: Black Hills Spruce
Bird: Ring-necked Pheasant
Population: 696,004
Area: 77,116 square miles

TENNESSEE

TENNESSEE RIVER

★ NASHVILLE

MEMPHIS

KEY FACTS

"The Volunteer State"
State: 16th
Date: June 1, 1796
Flower: Iris
Tree: Tulip Poplar
Bird: Mockingbird
Population: 4,877,185
Area: 42,114 square miles

Place Sticker Here

People come to Nashville, **Tennessee**, to hear bluegrass and country music at the famous Grand Ole Opry. They also visit Graceland in Memphis, the home of the "King of Rock'n'Roll," Elvis Presley.

You can see how people lived in pioneer days at Cades Cove in the Great Smoky Mountains. Great Smoky Mountain National Park is the largest park in Tennessee. The highest point in the state, called Clingman's Dome, is found here. The mountains are great for hunting and camping, too!

Tennessee is a leader in the production of metals. Tennessee miners dig for coal, zinc, and other minerals.

Texas is the second largest state in the country, and some of the busiest and biggest cities in the United States are here! "Black gold," or oil, was first discovered in Texas in 1866. Today Texas produces about 25 percent of the nation's domestic oil!

You can visit the Alamo in San Antonio, a Spanish mission where the battle for Texas' freedom from Mexico was fought in 1836. Davy Crockett died there.

Old forts, caverns, rodeos, and fairs can be found all over Texas. You can visit the Lyndon B. Johnson Space Center in Houston, which is a large center for space research.

Texas has more farms than any other state, the biggest ranches – and it is famous for its armadillos!

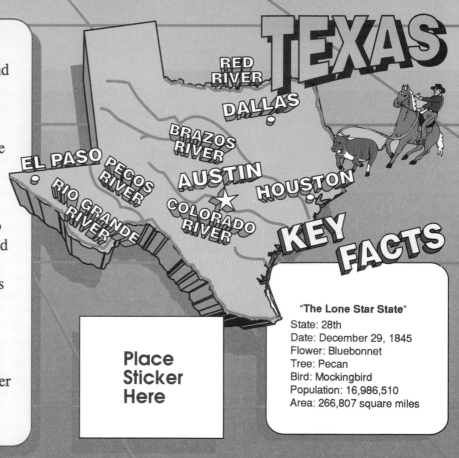

TEXAS

RED RIVER

DALLAS

BRAZOS RIVER

EL PASO PECOS RIVER

RIO GRANDE RIVER

AUSTIN ★

COLORADO RIVER

HOUSTON

KEY FACTS

Place Sticker Here

"The Lone Star State"
State: 28th
Date: December 29, 1845
Flower: Bluebonnet
Tree: Pecan
Bird: Mockingbird
Population: 16,986,510
Area: 266,807 square miles

UTAH

GREAT SALT LAKE

SALT LAKE CITY

SEVIER RIVER

COLORADO RIVER

KEY FACTS

Place Sticker Here

Utah has five national parks, six national monuments, and many canyons and caves. Most of Utah is desert, but many people enjoy skiing and snowmobiling in the mountains.

People also come to Utah to see natural bridges, petrified forests, streams, and beautiful forests. You can swim, but you can't sink, in the Great Salt Lake!

You can visit cliff dwellings built by Pueblo Indians hundreds of years ago. You can see real dinosaur bones at Dinosaur National Monument, and breathtaking cliffs and colorful rock formations at Bryce Canyon National Park.

Vermont was the first state after the original thirteen colonies to join the new United States. In 1777 Vermont's first constitution was written.

Vermont's beautiful mountain scenery is perfect for winter skiing. There are many ski resorts across the state. In summer, Vermont is the place to be for outdoor activities like camping, boating, and fishing.

You can visit Shelburne Museum, which has more than 30 early American buildings. Each building contains different collections, from antique dolls and carriages to glass and household items used by Vermont's early settlers.

Vermont is the country's largest producer of maple syrup.

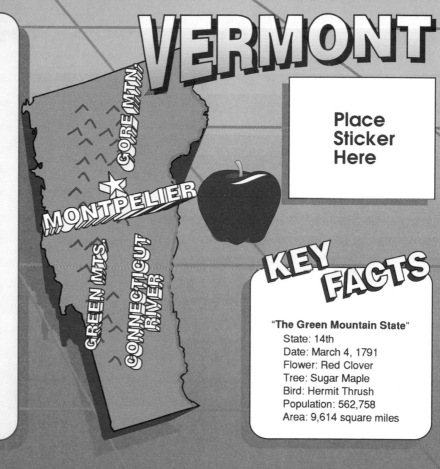

VERMONT

Place Sticker Here

KEY FACTS

"The Green Mountain State"
State: 14th
Date: March 4, 1791
Flower: Red Clover
Tree: Sugar Maple
Bird: Hermit Thrush
Population: 562,758
Area: 9,614 square miles

VIRGINIA

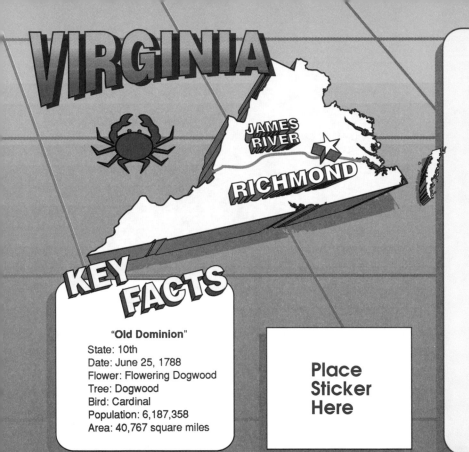

JAMES RIVER

RICHMOND

KEY FACTS

"Old Dominion"
State: 10th
Date: June 25, 1788
Flower: Flowering Dogwood
Tree: Dogwood
Bird: Cardinal
Population: 6,187,358
Area: 40,767 square miles

Place Sticker Here

More presidents were born in **Virginia** than anywhere else! Famous for its historical monuments and colonial homes, Jamestown, Virginia was the first permanent English settlement in the United States.

You can drive along the beautiful Blue Ridge Mountains, which are part of the Appalachians. Visit famous battlefields and see Monticello, Thomas Jefferson's home. George Washington's home, Mount Vernon, is also open to visitors.

Williamsburg was the capital of Virginia in the 1700's, and it was one of the most important cities in the colonies. Today it has been recreated to look as it did then, and it is one of the leading historic restorations in the country.

Washington's scenic Cascade Mountains are a major tourist attraction. Washington is also the home of one of the country's only active volcanoes, Mount St. Helens! Many people visit Washington for excellent fishing, hunting, skiing, and mountain climbing.

Three national parks have been preserved in Washington's beautiful mountains. You can visit the Grand Coulee Dam, which is the largest concrete dam in the United States.

It's fun to visit the recreation area and Pacific Science Center at Seattle Center. The 607-foot-high Space Needle is here. Or visit Fort Vancouver National Historic Site, an 1825 fur-trading post.

WASHINGTON

SEATTLE

COLUMBIA RIVER

OLYMPIA

MT. ST. HELENS

KEY FACTS

Place Sticker Here

"The Evergreen State"

State: 42nd
Date: November 11, 1889
Flower: Coast Rhododendron
Tree: Western Hemlock
Bird: Willow Goldfinch
Population: 4,866,692
Area: 68,139 square miles

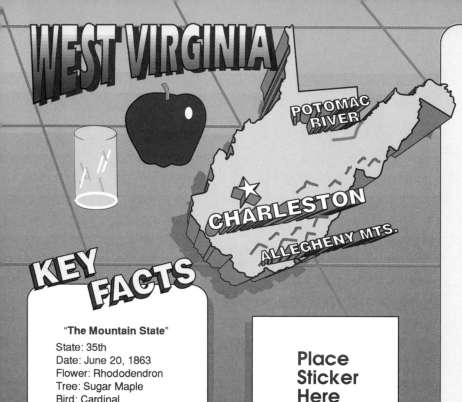

WEST VIRGINIA

POTOMAC RIVER

★ CHARLESTON

ALLEGHENY MTS.

Place Sticker Here

Except for the river valleys, there is almost no flat land in **West Virginia**. But many people come here to see the beautiful mountains. The Appalachian Mountains and the Allegheny Plateau cover most of the state.

You can hunt, fish, and explore caves. Many people visit Seneca Rock, a colorful rock that is 1,000 feet high and towers over the valley below it! You can also ride a coal car through an 1890's coal mine at Beckley Exhibition Mine. Or ride Cass Scenic Railroad, an old logging train engine, to the top of a mountain!

The mountains prevent much agriculture, but coal mining is very important to West Virginia.

Wisconsin has more than 15,000 lakes for fishing, boating, and swimming. The quiet, beautiful forests are perfect for biking, hunting, and fishing. Many people come to hike and camp. In winter, people ski, ice-boat, and ice-fish!

Wisconsin is known for its dairy products. Most of the country's milk, cheese, and butter come from Wisconsin. Milk cows can be seen grazing all over the state, which is sometimes called "America's Dairyland."

The Ringling Brothers gave their first show in Wisconsin in 1884. This later became the Famous Ringling Brothers Circus. Today you can visit Circus World Museum in Baraboo and see circus equipment. During the summer, circus acts are performed here every day!

WISCONSIN

Place Sticker Here

GREEN BAY

WISCONSIN RIVER

MADISON

MILWAUKEE

KEY FACTS

"The Badger State"
State: 30th
Date: May 29, 1848
Flower: Wood Violet
Tree: Sugar Maple
Bird: Robin
Population: 4,891,769
Area: 56,153 square miles

WYOMING

YELLOWSTONE NAT'L. PARK

BIGHORN RIVER

NORTH PLATTE RIVER

CHEYENNE

KEY FACTS

"The Equality State"

State: 44th
Date: July 10, 1890
Flower: Indian Paintbrush
Tree: Cottonwood
Bird: Meadowlark
Population: 453,588
Area: 97,809 square miles

Place Sticker Here

Wyoming is the home of the nation's first national park, Yellowstone. There are over 3,000 hot springs and geysers in Yellowstone National Park, including the famous "Old Faithful." The park also has canyons, waterfalls, and wild animals.

Wyoming is also famous for its beautiful mountains and spectacular scenery. Skiing, mountain climbing, hunting, and fishing are popular in this state.

Wyoming was the first state to grant women the right to vote. This happened in 1869, even before Wyoming was a state!

You can also visit Grand Teton National Park to see glaciers, and Hot Springs State Park to see mineral hot springs!